Green Design

Published in the United Kingdom by

The Design Council

28 Haymarket

London SW1Y 4SU

Printed and bound in Great Britain by

Bourne Press Ltd, Bournemouth

(paper: Classic Matt 130 gsm, containing up to 40 per cent straw pulp)

Designed by Nicole Griffin and Lucy Ward

British Library Cataloguing in Publication Data

Burall, Paul
Green Design
    1. Products. Design
    I. Title II. Design Council III. Series
    658.5752

ISBN 0 85072 284 5

Cover: satellite map showing severe depletion or 'hole' (shaded blue) in the ozone layer over Antarctica. (NASA, coloured by John Wells/ Science Photo Library)

Contents

Acknowledgements

The author and publishers gratefully acknowledge permission to reproduce the following pictures:

page 9: SPA; page 31: Moggridge Associates; page 32: Zanussi Ltd; page 34: Styling International; page 35: Ricardo-AS&A; page 39: Seward Glynn Marsh; page 46: ICI; pages 51 and 70: Mercedes-Benz (United Kingdom) Ltd; page 57: Steel Can Recycling Information Bureau; page 59: Better Bin Designs Ltd; page 62 (top): Safeway; page 63 (top): Tesco.

The author

Paul Burall, former Head of Campaigns and Corporate Publicity at the Design Council, has been responsible for a number of Design Council exhibitions on design and the environment, including The Green Designer (1986) and Red, Amber, Green (1988). A frequent conference speaker and commentator on green issues, he has also contributed to several publications on the subject.

Preface

The media did not wait for the 1980s to end before christening the 1990s the Decade of the Environment. Certainly it has been difficult to open a newspaper, turn on the television or go to a conference without being confronted with someone discussing green issues. Clearly the word no longer refers only to a fringe element – but will the interest last, and what are the implications for industry, commerce and design?

These are the issues which I endeavour to tackle in this book, not in the sense of providing a guide to designing green products or services – we are still far too low on the learning curve for that – but by outlining the kinds of opportunities and risks that confront managers and designers in this new green world, and by suggesting the kinds of questions and approaches that seem likely to lead to satisfactory conclusions.

In writing this book I have made two assumptions. The first is that, even if the media and the public become bored with green, the subject will remain of crucial importance to everyone in design, manufacturing and business, because the basic environmental challenges are here to stay and are of global proportions. This means that national govern-ments and international agencies will continue to introduce laws and regulations that will have far-reaching consequences for everyone. My second assumption is that industry, technology and design are a necessary part of the answer to our current environmental problems. Faced with a rapidly increasing world population, depleting resources, desperate poverty in the developing countries and an ageing population in the western world, there are, for the great majority of people, no answers in turning away from science and industry.

Paul Burall
September 1990

1 The pace of change

Anyone doubting the importance of environmental issues in shaping the future of industry, the economy and our lifestyles should look at the agendas of the meetings of world leaders in 1990. Whether the context is the European Community, the United Nations, the economic summits of the leading industrial nations or bilateral discussions between heads of state, a substantial proportion of many meetings has been devoted to environmental problems such as pollution and global warming. That issues such as these should now receive so much attention is remarkable and proves that the environmental debate is not simply a passing phase.

Press coverage reflecting the effect of environmental issues on government and business

■ The major issues

Of all the environmental problems facing us today, global warming is likely to have the most devastating effects. In order to combat these, the emission of harmful gases must be reduced and natural ways of absorbing them – such as the rainforests,

Environmental issue not a passing phase, minister warns

By David Thomas

COMPANIES MUST realise that the new environmental consciousness is not a passing fashion, Mr David Heathcoat-Amory, the junior environment minister, told the opening day of the Financial Times conference on industry and the environment.

Many compan responding to environmer

FINANCIAL TIMES MONDAY APRIL

GREEN'S AWARDS 1990

green hue brings benefit

…shaw analyses the awards for technological achi

in each sector according to source of finn

Sectors carrying out the work

| | Industry | 156.0 |
| Other | | |

Government may force use of 'green' packagin

By David Thomas, Resources Editor

RETAILERS MAY be forced to be environmentally friendly in the packaging of their goods after a government review of green policies which is now under way.

Government has

auditing their packaging of products, … t in our white paper … fur-

Source of funds for UK R & D

£3.45bn £3.66bn

industry did not b such changes volunta want the industry t

…OECD …cent in France and it… per cent in West Germa Glass-maker Pilking example, has won th for a head-up displa called in fighter ai is a sher …twee

3

which absorb carbon dioxide in vast quantities – be protected. Global warming will place a premium on energy efficiency, for controlling global warming inescapably means reducing the burning of fossil fuels. The two industries that are most obviously going to be affected are the power suppliers and the vehicle manufacturers, but since energy is consumed by almost everything we manufacture, design or do, the effects will be felt everywhere. As fossil fuel prices rise the market for smaller, fuel-efficient cars will grow alongside an increasing demand for appropriately labelled, energy-efficient appliances, lighting, and manufacturing plant and machinery. Increased transport costs may reinforce the move towards local or home working and away from commuting, while designers will have to pay more attention to minimizing the bulk and weight of products to reduce freight costs and fuel consumption. The boom in energy control systems and building insulation will spread from the business market to the domestic, while energy costs may reverse the trend towards air-conditioning in temperate climates.

There is also now an increasing acceptance of the seriousness of other environmental problems such as pollution from industrial and domestic waste and inefficient use of resources. These tend to pose a threat to human health or to flora and fauna, as well as often contributing to global warming, and range from the emission of gases causing acid rain or damage to the ozone layer from CFCs (chlorofluorocarbons), to more localized problems such as ozone created by office equipment or dangerous levels of radon accumulating in some British homes. However, it has taken many years for the public, politicians and industry to acknowledge that these are problems which affect us all.

▌ The growth of public concern

Why did public opinion in countries such as Britain and the United States become so suddenly green? Why, between 1986 and 1989, was there a rise from 8 per cent to 30 per cent in the number of people in Britain who believed that environmental problems should be the top priority for government (National Opinion Polls 1986 and 1989)? Green concerns and green campaigning on subjects such as non-returnable drinks bottles and the need for energy conservation have come and gone before, but it was only in the 1980s that some kind of scientific consensus emerged about the major environmental issues: the prime responsibility for acid rain was finally fixed on pollution from burning fossil fuels; global warming, previously perceived as a concern for the cranky few, became a cause for serious scientific debate; and recognition of the damage to health caused by atmospheric lead pollution persuaded car and fuel manufacturers to rethink their opposition to lead-free petrol rapidly (though carbon dioxide and other gases emitted were almost forgotten meanwhile). Nevertheless, the whole subject was still seen by most politicians, economists and opinion-formers in countries such as Britain and the United States as being largely irrelevant when compared with such traditional priorities as unemployment, urban regeneration and defence, while manufacturers remained generally unaffected by the environmental debate.

Amongst the public, meanwhile, the tide of environmental awareness was gradually rising. In North America this had as much to do with the tidemark of medical waste on beaches alongside poisoned seals and lobsters as with any new scientific evidence of impending disaster. Droughts in the mid-West focused concern on global warming, smog rose to record levels in large cities, and the final straw was probably the Exxon Valdez oil spill with subsequent pictures of dying sea otters and birds. This combined with worldwide concern about damage to the ozone layer caused by CFC-filled aerosols and increasing alarm at the rapid destruction of the Brazilian rainforest (amongst others).

Though lagging far behind countries such as Holland and Germany, public pressure in Britain and America was gathering momentum and manufacturers of products as varied as detergents, batteries, disposable nappies, tinned tuna and many kinds of packaging realized they had to react rapidly to pressure for what consumers perceived to be greener products. British retailers reacted by removing from their shelves a wide range of products from hardwood chopping boards to CFC-filled aerosols; manufacturers fought to keep up with the demand for greener products; and designers began to realize that green design meant something more than recycled paper.

When manufacturers started trying to adapt to growing environmental concern, some, including advertising agencies, burned their fingers with absurd claims or lack of thought. The Rover Group won the 1989 Friends of the Earth Green Con Award by claiming that one of its cars was 'as ozone-friendly as it is economical' because it used lead-free petrol (lead being nothing to do with ozone depletion). Other companies have done rather better: McDonalds, faced with especially fierce criticism in the United States, reacted with laudable initiatives such as making its drinking straws lighter (reducing waste by around 450,000 kilograms a year), starting a recycling scheme with in-restaurant bins for polystyrene packaging, and using recycled paper not only for napkins but throughout its headquarters. The company then decided to make a feature of its new recyclable cardboard containers with a special label bearing the three-arrow recycling symbol: unfortunately, the glue used to stick the label proved to inhibit recycling.

In August 1989 and again in February 1990, the London advertising agency Ogilvy and Mather carried out a survey of the general public and business people in Britain, with some significant results (*Marketing to Green Consumers*, 1990). Overall, the interest in green issues increased in the six months between the two surveys, with 'the environment' topping the list of serious concerns. (Perhaps surprisingly, the 80 per cent figure for the public was topped by an 88 per cent figure for business people.) The number of people saying that they 'always try a green alternative' moved up from 48 per cent in 1989 to 55 per cent in 1990, while those saying that they were willing to pay extra for a green alternative rose from 42 per cent to 47 per cent. But, significantly, these trends were reversed among the very people who, seemingly, would be most likely to be green: there was a drop in support for green products among the green activists. Ogilvy and Mather speculated that this group, being the most committed, was the most disappointed

Consumers divided

Ogilvy and Mather identified five kinds of consumer in terms of their green attitudes:

- Activists (16%): slightly upmarket; aware; believe technology will help; put environment before growth

- Realists (34%): average all round; worried/concerned but see conflict between profit and green; critical of bandwagonning; pessimistic about solutions

- Complacents (28%): upmarket; not knowledgeable; believe that somebody else – humanity, business, Government, public – will solve all the problems

- Alienateds (22%): downmarket; uneducated; lack of green knowledge; too many other worries; see green as a transient issue; overwhelmed by a sense of despair.

Source: Ogilvy and Mather 1990

to find that some of the green alternatives just did not work as well as their traditional alternatives and that some green claims were proving dubious.

In the UK it seemed that public concern had finally begun to exert an influence on the business world: a survey carried out by the UK magazine *The Director* (February 1990) showed that company directors cited their families and public opinion as significant sources of pressure to adapt to environmental pressures.

▌Greener government

One of the most significant developments in the Government's approach to environmental issues came in September 1988, when Prime Minister Margaret Thatcher made a turning-point speech to the Royal Society, accepting that environmental problems demanded action:

> For generations, we have assumed that the efforts of mankind would leave the fundamental equilibrium of the world's systems and atmosphere stable. But it is possible that with all the enormous changes (population, agricultural, use of fossil fuels) concentrated into such a short period of time, we have unwittingly begun a massive experiment with the system of this planet itself. (*Science and Public Affairs 4, 3–9*, Royal Society, 1989)

That speech marked the start of changes in British government policy that will, in the long run, have far-reaching consequences for industry, commerce and design, but in this the British government was simply catching up with countries as far apart as Holland and Japan which have led the way in implementing actions to control environmental damage.

Green go the batteries

Early in 1988 Varta launched a mercury-free chloride battery in Scandinavia and its home market Germany, but decided that the UK was not ready for such a product. Margaret Thatcher's environmental conversion speech to the Royal Society seemed to change the company's mind: within weeks, Varta had launched Britain's first mercury-free battery, stressing its greenness by including flower seeds within the bubble packs. Varta's share of the British market grew by 50 per cent in six months, adding some £10 million a year to its sales.

Not to be outdone, Ever Ready launched a cadmium-free zinc chloride battery in October 1989 followed, three months later, with a battery free of both cadmium and mercury. Duracell, meanwhile, set about the more difficult task of getting rid of mercury from long-life alkaline batteries: by the end of 1989 it had cut the quantity from 5 per cent by weight to just 0.02 per cent.

Elsewhere, Memorex was advertising the environmental virtues of rechargeable batteries, and a consortium of European manufacturers — encouraged by a proposed European Community Directive — had set up a recycling scheme for used batteries.

By the end of 1989, around half of the annual £250 million British domestic battery market had been taken by products claiming to be environmentally friendlier.

Sources: Varta, Ever Ready, Memorex 1990

Varta mercury- and cadmium-free batteries

9

The most far-reaching government proposals have been approved in Holland. The country's tightly packed 260-page National Environmental Policy Plan, published in 1988, will double the proportion of the nation's wealth devoted to controlling pollution and add the equivalent of £120 to the annual cost of living of every family by the mid-1990s. When first proposed, the Plan caused the coalition government to fall because one party felt that the suggested environmental measures – higher taxes on new cars to encourage public transport, increased petrol excise duties, new taxes on diesel, and increased levies on industries that pollute water and air – were too expensive and would harm industrial competitiveness; but the public backed the Plan and its supporters won the subsequent general election in September 1989.

Japan (encouraged by its 90 per cent reliance on imported fuels) has also shown what can be achieved. In 1979, the Japanese passed the vaguely titled but far-from-toothless Law Concerning the Use of Energy: this included a requirement for major power users to employ qualified energy managers and to keep detailed records of fuel use and conservation measures, with heavy fines for non-compliance. In addition, all electrical appliances had to carry energy consumption information, and tax concessions were made available for energy-saving equipment. As a result of this and other measures, Japan used 6 per cent less energy in 1988 than in 1973, despite a growth in Gross Domestic Product of 46 per cent.

■ The future

Now that legislation to alleviate environmental problems is being introduced in many countries, the effect on industry worldwide will be increasingly apparent. At a European level, 15 major measures have been taken by the European Community on problems as varied as titanium dioxide, car emissions, CFCs, and emissions from power stations, while the Community Directive on Containers of Liquids for Human Consumption will have far-reaching consequences for the packaging industry. Italy has ruled that all plastic containers will have to be biodegradable by 1995, while drinks in Denmark already have to be sold in returnable bottles. In Britain green audits have been introduced by every government department to look at everything from the exhaust emissions of vehicles and the use of recycled paper to the efficient use of energy.

These measures are just the start of many which will affect industry. The European Commission has proposed the introduction of civil liability for damage caused by waste, irrespective of fault, and the British government is itself discussing legislation which will force polluters to pay compensation for environmental damage, whether accidental or deliberate, as well as introducing increasingly stringent requirements for the treatment of polluting emissions and other wastes. Other moves may include banning all chlorine-producing compounds (since chlorine damages the ozone layer); and extending the restrictions on materials that may be used in food packaging. More general constraints on packaging that are being openly discussed by British Ministers include banning the use of mixed plastics in bottles to facilitate recycling; restricting excessive packaging; and forcing retailers to accept more recycling.

The extent, severity and speed of action at government level is difficult to forecast but should not be underestimated, as was shown by the rapidity with which the 1987 Montreal protocol on CFC reductions was agreed once the problem had been clearly identified. The likelihood is that the most significant actions will be generated by one or more of three prime causes: public pressure, increasingly echoed by politicians; transnational pollution (where the inter-governmental nature of the problem automatically brings the subject within the orbit of the international agencies, which in the long run are less vulnerable to commercial and electoral pressures); and scientific evidence of major risk (as with global warming).

Any one of these triggers for action can have profound implications for designers and for business. For example, pressure to control pollution from car emissions has come from several different sources in different parts of the world. In mid-1990 Californians voted to double petrol taxes, partly to fund public transport and road improvements, while the 123-point, three-stage Los Angeles Environment Plan, agreed in 1989, aims to make the Los Angeles air 70 per cent cleaner by 2009, with moves also being made to introduce financial incentives encouraging the use of pool cars and public transport (*Independent*, 4 October 1989). The European Community is considering energy efficiency standards for vehicles – as well as electrical appliances – and in the UK there have been calls for a return to a rising scale of excise to favour small cars: a 100cc cut in engine size can reduce carbon dioxide emissions by 3 per cent (*Economist*, 26 January 1990).

■ Economic pressures

One of the strongest signals of the profound effect that environmental pressures will have on industry has come from Professor David Pearce of the Department of Economics, University College, London. His landmark report *Blueprint for a Green Economy* – commissioned by the

British Department of the Environment – strongly supports using the tax system to force consumers to pay the true environmental costs for goods and services, suggesting that the resulting income should be spent on repairing the environment and measures to prevent damage. 'An unfettered market is one that will harm the environment', he emphasizes, going on to argue that 'market forces are very powerful weapons, so we should use them and make them work for the environment'.

Also important in the long run will be the pressures from companies that have already embarked on green initiatives. They will take every opportunity to feature their green credentials throughout their marketing activities, challenging their rivals to match them as officially approved green labelling schemes overcome consumer distrust. Where such initiatives are less related to consumer products – for example, where factory effluents have been cleaned up – the pressure will be on governments and other agencies to force rival companies to bring their standards up to the best. It is already clear that countries within Europe with high environmental standards see the low achievers as providing unfair competition which should be outlawed under the rules governing the post-1992 Open Market.

Nor can investment pressures be ignored. In the UK there is now a wide variety of 'ethical' unit trusts, while in the United States 'socially responsible' groups of investors control some £300 billion of investments.

So there are many reasons for designers and managers to take the greening of industry and business seriously. Not everyone will find their businesses having to make substantial and expensive changes in the face of environmental legislation, as have the car and chemical manufacturers.

Not everyone is faced with the kind of seemingly intractable challenge that global warming presents to the coal industry. But there is probably not a single business that will remain unchanged by the new environmental challenges.

The last word should be with an avowed environmentalist who just happens to have made many millions of pounds in business. Godfrey Bradman is chairman both of the property development company Rosehaugh and of the Friends of the Earth Trust. At the beginning of the Decade of the Environment, he said:

> It has seemed to me that we have been treating the world's resources and its delicate ecological systems with the recklessness of a pools winner whose motto is 'spend, spend, spend' and who gives little if any thought to the longer term . . . I believe that we are witnessing one of those rare moments in the development of political debate, when an issue which has been of interest only to a concerned minority, suddenly and irrevocably forces its way onto the political agenda and stays there (speech to the National Council of Building Material Producers, 14 March 1989).

2 General principles

The key principle for a green world is, in a word, sustainability. Professor David Pearce has defined a sustainable economic system as one in which:

> The well-being of today's generations is not increased at the expense of future generations . . . Each generation should ensure it passes on to the next a stock of assets no less than that which it inherited. (*Blueprint for a Green Economy*)

The Brundtland Commission, in its report *Our Common Future*, published by the UN World Commission on Environment and Development in 1987, defined sustainable development as:

> Development that meets the needs of the present without compromising the ability of future generations to meet their own needs.

Designers therefore have a crucial role to play in achieving a more sustainable economic and social order. The complexity and importance of the designer's role (see also Chapter 7) is highlighted by a second principle that those concerned about the environment set alongside that of sustainability. This is the need for a holistic approach to solutions. It is no use greening a part of a process if the whole is still unnecessarily damaging: designers must ensure that by providing solutions to one set of environmental problems they are not creating or increasing others. This concept is vital to designers, who often have a critical influence over every aspect of a product's life, from manufacture and use to repair and disposal, and from the choice of materials and the efficiency with which energy is used to the longevity of the product's life and the effects of its eventual disposal.

∎ Criteria for green design

So where should the designer, manufacturer or service company begin? Usual definitions of good design already include criteria such as successful performance, ease of use, safety, simplicity of maintenance, appropriate materials, efficiency of manufacture, attractive appearance and value for money. Of course the importance of each criterion varies depending on what it is applied to: safety is hardly the prime concern of a newspaper designer but is crucial for a team designing a nuclear power plant. Designing for green markets and with an eye on likely future legislative demands does not invalidate the traditional criteria for good design, but it does demand that some are given different weightings and that new considerations are also taken into account. For example, the designer can no longer develop a

The basic principles
The environmentally aware designer should aim to:

- increase efficiency in use of materials, energy and other resources
- minimize damage or pollution from chosen materials
- reduce to a minimum any long-term harm to the environment caused by use of the product
- ensure the planned life of the product is the most appropriate in environmental terms, and if necessary that the product functions efficiently for its full life
- take full account of the effects of the end disposal of the product
- ensure the packaging, instructions and overall appearance of the product encourage efficient and environment-friendly use.
- minimize nuisances such as noise or smell
- analyse and minimize potential safety hazards

product in isolation from the effects that the materials and production processes may have on the environment, or without thinking through the implications of eventual disposal.

∎ The complex equation

There is a danger of oversimplifying what makes a design environmentally acceptable. For instance, while for many products long life is an important environmental objective, this should not mean that too long a life prevents benefits from being gained with new materials, new techniques or revised assessments of environmental risk. CFCs provide an excellent example: they were first used in aerosols because of the safety advantages that they offered over previous propellants in being non-toxic and non-flammable. At the time of their introduction, CFCs were welcomed as a great advance by those concerned with safety; it was years before it became apparent that the breakdown of CFCs into chlorine was causing immense damage to the ozone layer.

Designs that are expected to have a long life are at risk not only from scientific discoveries but also from legislation and changes in consumer perceptions. So one objective should be to build as much flexibility as is reasonably possible into a design at the beginning in order to assist incremental improvements throughout its life.

More fundamental questions arise when two major environmental objectives clash. At the simplest level is the kind of conundrum faced by someone who has designed a product that is notably more sympathetic to the environment than its rivals, yet can only be sold with some not-very-green packaging. Some environmentalists – who see large-scale renewable energy sources as one of the keys to reducing the threat of global warming – insist that schemes such as a barrage across Britain's Severn estuary and its associated tidal power station are essential; other environmentalists – concerned about the increasing loss of habitats for wading birds and other wildlife – see the barrage as an environmental threat rather than a solution. Environmentally responsible decisions will rarely be straightforward, and the different benefits and disadvantages will, as always, need to be balanced out carefully.

Local solutions may cause global problems, as in the case of the electric car. For anyone living in Los Angeles, such vehicles could help to eliminate the smog that threatens to suffocate them, while town-dwellers elsewhere would also welcome the local environmental improvement brought about by the inherent quietness and lack of polluting emissions. However, on a global scale electric cars could simply add to the problems of global warming and acid rain: in overall terms they are less efficient than petrol-driven cars and the fossil-fuel power stations that are likely to be required to generate their power present one of the biggest threats to the planet's environment. Electric cars fuelled from a renewable source of electricity would offer a solution to this problem.

Green design does not present designers with any easy answers. As always, it is up to the individual designer or design team to find out the facts and make sensible judgements, having weighed up the overall benefits of different alternatives. It is especially important to avoid making simplistic assumptions. How many people, for example, would assume that a paper bag is, generally, less damaging to the environment than a plastic bag? Yet the West German Environmental Protection Agency, having looked at the complete lifecycle of paper and plastic bags, concluded that the plastic bag used only a third of the energy of the paper bag and caused less pollution in its processing. The manufacture of 50,000 paper bags produced between 80 kilograms and 230 kilograms of sulphur dioxide emissions, compared with 17 for plastic; paper bag production also resulted in greater carbon monoxide and hydrocarbon emissions. Finally, plastic bags were more likely to be re-used by the consumer than paper bags.

The obvious need for efficiency in manufacture and performance of the final product simply has a more extensive and comprehensive significance when environmental effects are part of the equation. It may seem obvious that a product which uses materials and energy economically in manufacture and use is helping to conserve resources, but less obvious is the double advantage that materials and energy minimization provides for cutting pollution: first, minimization reduces the quantity of chemicals available for release; second, maximizing the percentage of those chemicals that end up in the product, or that are converted into useful energy, automatically minimizes the percentage left over as, at best, harmless waste or, at worst, damaging pollution.

▮ A greener management structure

Some companies and organizations have used the link between efficiency and environmental benevolence to boost their profits or offer their customers better value for money. In the public sector, local authorities have saved many millions of pounds through energy efficiency measures – ranging from replacing inefficient boilers with modern designs to minimizing heat loss by encouraging staff to keep windows shut in cold weather – and have thus made some contribution to reducing pollution and the build-up of greenhouse gases. In the private sector, the laurels must go to 3M, which introduced its first global corporate environment policy in 1975 and has since achieved remarkable reductions both in pollution and costs: in terms of economic payback from its waste reduction policies, 3M claims savings of $500 million from 2,800 projects; pollutants and waste have been cut by 500,000 tonnes.

The story of 3M also illustrates the importance of a company organizing its management to respond properly to the threats and opportunities of a green world. In a break from its traditional corporate structure, 3M established its Environmental Engineering and Pollution Control (EE&PC) department as an independent operating unit, separate from engineering and manufacture. The head of the EE&PC reports directly to one of 3M's five executive vice-presidents, L D DeSimone, who explains that:

3M's Three Ps

3M's Pollution Prevention Plus programme was introduced in 1988 to build on the company's success in reducing costs by reducing waste through the 15-year-old Pollution Prevention Pays programme.

The new policy aims to reduce the company's worldwide emissions by 90 per cent by the year 2000, including cutting solvent emissions by more than 55,000 tonnes a year.

3M's previous successes have ranged from the replacement of solvents with a hot-melt system for putting adhesive on the backing of sanding discs – saving £150,000 and reducing solvent emissions by 75 tonnes a year – to using non-recyclable plastics wastes from a plant manufacturing face masks and respirators as fuel for a heating and process boiler – saving £60,000 in costs and 250,000 tonnes of landfill every year.

Source: 3M September 1990

By putting environmental engineering on a par with the other operating units, we have elevated our environment decisions to a high level. The net effect is that environmental concerns are considered at every step in the development and manufacture of our products.

The objectives of 3M's EE&PC include ensuring compliance with environmental legislation; minimizing potential liabilities; and maintaining and enhancing the company's environmental reputation.

The department splits its activities between those affecting products and those affecting production plants and other facilities. The company has also set up a complementary Corporate Product Responsibility department, whose purpose is to assist individual business unit and production managers in understanding the increasing impact of environmental regulation on their operations, and to ensure that all 3M products are technically and ethically sound.

In the UK, 3M's environmental policies are being implemented through a matrix organisation in the engineering, manufacturing and research sectors. This is managed by a central committee, chaired by the company's Environment Manager, comprising representatives of staff and line divisions: its task is to develop a vision, a set of goals and a detailed strategy to reinforce 3M's UK environmental programmes.

Another major international manufacturing company that has taken steps to manage its response to environmental legislation and market pressures properly is Philips. Philips' main board has adopted policy objectives that include providing products which, together with practical advice on their application, will not cause undue impact on the environment. The board insists that an environmental policy must be an integral part of the general policy of each of the

Tasks of the Environmental Coordinator

Among the tasks designated for the Environmental Coordinator within each of Philips' product divisions are:

a) to report and advise senior management on the environmental aspects of new and existing production processes and products

b) to maintain contact with experts from other multinational industries, industry federations, and supra-national organizations

c) to establish cross-links between Philips plants with similar processes, with the aim of optimizing these

d) to coordinate and initiate investigations for necessary specific process adjustments

e) to ensure that product and process release procedures are available and that there is a procedure for assessing their performance

f) to advise on the acceptability of raw materials and processes and to keep records of environmentally relevant materials used in products or in processing

g) to advise on the budgeting of investments connected with environmental protection.

Source: Philips 1990

company's groups; that each group must continually develop an environmental programme which is evaluated formally on an annual basis; and that responsibilities for environmental protection are clear and performance monitored.

Philips' top management insists that legal environmental responsibility cannot be delegated below that of the senior national management in each country. Product divisions are charged with ensuring that due regard is given to environmental regulations in different countries and that environmental protection forms an integral part of the management of the product divisions. This includes either placing the subject 'explicitly and regularly on the agenda of the management team' or setting up a special environmental steering group. Each product division has to appoint an Environmental Coordinator (see box on previous page) and ensure that an environmental checklist is used by those concerned with the development of production processes.

Like 3M, Philips has set up a central unit to provide environmental expertise both at the corporate level and for the product divisions. This unit is charged with keeping abreast of the environmental situation worldwide; building up expertise in the technical, legal and organizational fields; and coordinating or initiating environmental studies for use by Philips' national organizations and product divisions. As with 3M, the Philips main Board states that one of its guiding principles is that *prevention is better than cure.* As a supplier of scientific measuring equipment, electronic components and other products, Philips also assists other companies in marketing environmentally friendlier products and services.

IBM, too, has a well-formulated environmental policy that includes the prevention principle as one of its main objectives. 'If you don't generate pollution, you don't have to manage it', is how Tony Cleaver, chairman and chief executive of IBM UK, describes IBM's aim of using non-polluting and energy-efficient technologies wherever possible when designing products and processes. IBM's other environmental objectives are: to meet or exceed all applicable government regulations; to set its own stringent standards where no government standards exist; and to help governments and other industries develop solutions to environmental problems wherever IBM's knowledge might be helpful.

Tony Cleaver has set out a personal view of how managers should deal rationally with environmental pressures and concerns:

First, we should determine the philosophy of our approach. Then we should choose the method to enable us to respond effectively. And, third, we should establish policies which enable us to use that method. (*UK CEED Bulletin No26*, November–December 1989)

Like 3M and Philips, Tony Cleaver insists that top management commitment is crucial to success, listing other essentials as the need for company-wide training and awareness programmes; procedures for gathering information; formalizing the assessment of failures and concentrating on prevention; and measuring and feeding back results so that incremental improvements can be made on a continuous basis.

British companies have a long way to go in managing the environmental aspects of their business. A 1990 survey, *European Management Attitudes to Environmental Issues*, by the management consultants Touche Ross, found that West German, Dutch and Danish companies were well ahead in setting up management structures to deal with environmental issues. Eighty per cent of Danish companies and 75 per cent of West German companies had appointed a board member with specific responsibility for environmental management, compared with less than half the UK companies surveyed. In addition, 75 per cent of West German companies – and 90 per cent of those in Denmark – had either altered or planned to alter their products in response to environmental pressures, compared with 52 per cent in the UK. Many German, Belgian and Danish companies had set environmental standards for their suppliers, but no British company had done the same. French companies stood out from the rest in expressing little interest in green products or processes but giving high priority to the avoidance of accidents, including accidents resulting in polluting emissions.

∎ Thinking ahead

Whether planning a company strategy or designing individual products or equipment, those responsible should examine which of the pressures for a greener world are likely to carry the most weight in the future. Actions by governments – whether national or international – are usually signposted well in advance of their implementation, but the speed of change in environmental agreements and legislation is in danger of being – and often is – underestimated (see box).

Perhaps the best policy when planning for future environmental implications is, where the perceived environmental

Car manufacturers caught out

There have been many approaches to cutting emissions from small cars. In Britain during the 1980s, Austin Rover and Ford invested many hundreds of millions of pounds in developing lean-burn engines: by increasing the air-to-petrol ratio, the engine burns fuel more efficiently, reducing both petrol consumption and polluting emissions.

Other countries and manufacturers had taken a different route by fitting catalytic converters to existing engines to convert noxious emissions into relatively harmless gases.

At the end of the decade, the European Community opted for catalytic converters and set a standard that effectively outlawed the lean-burn solution.

Meanwhile, the Japanese simply adopted the world's most stringent emission standards – those in the USA – and began to apply them to every car sold anywhere.

threat is significant in national or inter-national terms, to assume that the highest environmental standards that have been adopted or officially recommended any-where in the world are likely to become the accepted standards in the developed world sooner rather than later. Taking such a view has three potential advan-tages. First, it can, as car manufacturers found, simultaneously simplify produc-tion and open up more markets. Sec-ondly, selling a product or service that meets higher environmental standards than current national law demands can also offer a significant marketing advan-tage. Thirdly, this can prevent investment in products or processes that may be outlawed or require expensive adaptation as higher standards become more universal.

If the significance for designers and businesses of actions by govern-ments on such issues is clear, the effects of public pressures are less easy to divine. However, it is possible to make some reasonable assumptions by monitoring the main preoccupations of the green lobbies: at the very least, it is worth taking an occasional look at some of the environmental publications or maintaining a subscription to one of the magazines or databases that report activities in these areas (see Chapter 8). Such monitoring can provide advance warning of likely campaigns that might affect business, although, where the green lobbies become concerned about any issue with a significant technological or scientific content, cross-reference to a scientific periodical such as the *New Scientist* can provide a necessary balance; when scientists (even just a few, provided they are genuinely independent) start supporting the lobbies, the warning bells should ring.

Spotting opportunities and foreseeing threats are a vital part of every company's strategic planning and are equally important to designers in their role of creating products and services for the future. In this new era, the opportunities and threats created by the increasing environmental awareness of public and governments alike demand as much attention as planning for changes in inflation, exchange rates or labour supply.

3 Energy and its dependants

As suggested in the previous chapter, environmental pressures are likely to affect the energy market in dramatic and fundamental ways. For those working in the energy industries, the prime challenges are those of improving efficiencies and developing cleaner technologies. This applies equally to industries involved in the design and production of any kind of machinery, motor or domestic appliance, and to architects and interior designers specifying heating, insulation and lighting. This chapter looks at the implications of different energy sources, and the ways in which life-long energy consumption by the finished product can be minimized or reassessed. The energy implications of different materials and processes are discussed in Chapter 4.

The choice of fuel is complex. Judgements about efficiency have to take into account both the efficiency of the chosen fuel's production method and its efficiency in final use by the end product. What is more, fuels can come from different sources, each with wildly different environmental effects: electricity may be generated by inefficient, heavily-polluting coal-fired stations, by renewable hydro-electric sources or by nuclear power – which is usually clean but has the potential for horrific damage. The designer should always look to see if the choice of energy source is inevitable or if a better alternative is available. Hydroelectric schemes are well developed, and new technology is now making it possible to tap the energy from slow-moving rivers for the first time. Wind energy is well-established too in areas such as California, and solar energy is gradually being exploited. Geothermal sources have been used in some countries for many years also, but wave energy and energy from biomass sources, such as sustainably grown plants and trees – in the long term perhaps the most promising large-scale source of energy – still need considerable development to make them commercially viable.

▮ Minimizing inefficiency

Another alternative source is energy that has previously been wasted, usually in the form of excess heat. Large combined heat and power generation systems can show improvements in overall energy efficiency approaching 50 per cent compared with plants that only generate power, and significant savings are being made in process industries, commercial buildings and through the incineration of waste materials. The Building Research Establishment (BRE) has many case histories demonstrating energy savings in a whole variety of fields, from the use of waste heat for growing tomatoes in a Scottish whisky distillery to the integration of heating, ventilating and air conditioning systems in buildings (see Chapter 8).

Most energy in most homes is still used for heating, but there are many ways of attacking this, from designing new buildings to maximize passive solar heating and minimize heat losses, to retrofitting existing homes with improved insulation and improving the efficiency of boilers and control systems. The efficiency of boilers has been greatly improved: the latest gas condensing boilers – which use a second heat exchanger to collect heat that would otherwise escape in the flue gases – are up to 86 per cent efficient, compared with around 74 per cent for a standard modern boiler.

The Royal Institute of Technology in Sweden found that traditional wood-burning stoves – popular in Scandinavia – burned fuel only partly, because the cold water circulating in the heat exchanger cooled the flames and left some wood unburnt. The designer, Konstantin Mavroudis, solved this problem by separating the furnace from the heat exchanger, lining the former with a ceramic material to allow high-temperature combustion to help the wood burn thoroughly. Any unburnt gases and smoke rise into a conical upper combustion chamber where they are concentrated and burned, the heat exchanger being above the chamber. Complete with an electronic monitoring and control system that works through a fan to regulate the oxygen supply, the new boiler, manufactured by Combi Heat, uses less fuel and greatly minimizes such pollutants as carbon monoxide (*New Scientist*, 15 July 1989).

Design solutions to improving heating efficiency vary enormously. The kitchen sink manufacturer, Astrocast, used moulds heated by water, which then went to waste: installing a re-circulating system with the water temperature boosted as necessary halved energy costs. The use of insulated loading doors in low-energy factories can save up to 11 per cent of heating costs, while the design of special profile doors to fit around the tail of an aircraft to maintain temperature levels while the remainder is inside a hangar for maintenance has saved £37,500 per door per year (Energy Efficiency Office (BRE) Demonstration Scheme, *Project Profile 329*, October 1988).

Yet another approach has been used by Yorkshire Electricity to improve the energy efficiency of the winter aeration of stored grain. Conventionally, this aeration has used the same high-power fans used to dry the grain in summer. For winter aeration, these were inefficient, as only a low air volume is required, but providing an entirely separate system just for the winter was uneconomic. Yorkshire Electricity's answer was to attach a small, low-volume, parasite fan to the ducting system for the main fan. Winter power costs have been reduced by as much as 90 per cent, and the parasite system recovered its £640 cost in just one year (Yorkshire Electricity press release, July 1989).

▌Lighting

If architects have a major role to play in improving energy efficiency in buildings, interior and product designers have a part too, especially with regard to lighting.

An enlightened approach

The Claude Gill Bookshop in York has reduced its electricity consumption for lighting by over 60 per cent by replacing conventional display lighting with low energy ELPAR-H display lamps. The new lamps, which use the same sockets as their predecessors, had the additional advantage of producing 20 per cent less heat, so improving comfort in the shop.

Faced with 15-year-old twin fluorescent lighting systems in their Bath offices Wessex Water found that the usual options of adding control systems or renewing the lighting proved to be financially unattractive, as the company was on a low electricity price tariff. Instead, the designers chose simply to replace the old reflectors with new high-reflectance units. This halved the number of fluorescent tubes needed, cutting bills by around £4,500 a year at a capital cost of £17,000, as well as reducing air conditioning and maintenance costs.

Factories can benefit too. Replacing 1968 mercury lighting in a Vickers Shipbuilding Engineering factory in Barrow-in-Furness with modern high-pressure sodium lamps improved lighting levels by a much-needed five times with no increase in energy load; adding a computer-controlled energy management system that linked the lighting and heating systems then reduced total energy consumption.

Source: *Energy Management*, Department of Energy, June/July 1989 and November/December 1989

SL48 Solar Lantern, designed by Moggridge Associates for BP Solar International

Around 15 per cent of the electricity consumed in the United Kingdom goes on lighting, costing industry and commerce £1.2 billion a year.

Designers concerned with lighting should check at least three areas:

- specification of low-energy light sources

- automatic time or light-level controls to prevent unnecessary use

- upgrading the efficiency of existing systems.

Designs such as Moggridge Associates' Solar Lantern and the garden light, also solar-powered, made by Lamperti in Italy, have succeeded in using alternative energy sources, but major savings can also be made by the use of low-energy lamps or high reflectance units.

Lighting also provides an excellent example of the interdependence of engineering and industrial designers. The engineers have gone a long way towards reducing the energy that needs to be consumed for lighting. The most modern compact fluorescent lamps, for instance, use only a fifth of the electricity of their tungsten equivalents, give excellent

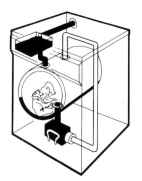

colour rendering, eliminate the flicker that bugged their predecessors, and can make total cost savings as high as four times their initial price over their lifetime. Yet these benefits are almost unknown to most British domestic consumers: as yet very few attractive domestic light fittings have been designed and produced to take the slightly larger low-energy lamps.

▮ Domestic appliances

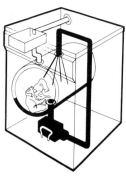

Zanussi Jetstream washing machine which minimizes water intake, reducing heat and washing powder needed.

Level of water intake is kept to 5 litres, plus whatever water has been absorbed by clothes (top).

When water intake is complete, heater is activated, simultaneously recirculating and heating water to required temperature (bottom).

The design of most domestic appliances is also open to considerable refinement in energy efficiency terms. The insulation of ovens can usually be substantially improved, while the room for improvement in appliances such as dishwashers and washing machines is evident when one compares the current best with the current worst: similar-capacity machines can use as much as twice the energy consumed by their better rivals. In these appliances, the key – which is nothing new – is both in the conception of the design and in careful detailing. Thus the inclusion of sensors in modern clothes driers to replace 'guess-how-long' timeclocks made substantial energy savings in the operation of these machines. In washing machines, savings have been made by cooperation between the washing powder and the appliance manufacturers to reduce wash temperatures, while individual manufacturers such as Zanussi have made advances in reducing water volumes to a minimum, controlling temperatures more accurately, and giving the user the ability to override parts of the cycle in the interests of economy. Japanese manufacturers are looking at using artificial intelligence computers to determine the type and dirt-levels of clothing in order to match the wash cycle even more accurately with the real need.

Of all domestic appliances, fridges and freezers have been the most neglected when it comes to energy efficiency. In Britain, eight per cent of all electricity produced is used by domestic fridges and freezers. Worse, typical British domestic fridges and freezers consume between two and three kilowatt hours per litre (kWh/litre) of storage space annually, compared with state-of-the-art appliances produced elsewhere with equivalent consumption levels as low as 0.2 kWh/litre. Danish and American researchers believe that it is quite possible to cut this to just 0.1 kWh/litre. The risk of not improving is considerable: new United States legislation outlawing inefficient fridges and freezers is removing almost all of the models that were available there in 1987 (*New Scientist*, 12 May 1990).

One of the problems facing the designers and manufacturers of fridges and freezers is the need to reduce the use of CFCs both as a refrigerant and for insulation. Various alternatives to the CFC R11 are being tried as blowing agents for polyurethane foam insulation, but most are not such efficient insulators and offer potential problems ranging from flammability and incompatibility with the plastic liners, to the fact that they retain a degree of ozone-depletion capacity on release. More radical solutions – such as building insulation panels by sealing

Cool efficiency

Gram, the Danish manufacturer, has produced a range of low-energy refrigerators, including the Gram LER 200, 'the world's most economic refrigerator,' with a power consumption of 0.24 kWh per 24 hours and net storage capacity of 196 litres. Energy efficiency comes from careful design in four key areas. First, the insulation is more than double the thickness of conventional fridges. Second, the motor and compressor have been designed to be efficient, the motor to use magnets more powerful than normal and the compressor designed to avoid dissipating energy in turbulence. Third, the heat exchange system uses larger evaporators and condensers. Finally, the door seals and catches have been designed to perform satisfactorily throughout the life of the appliance.

Source: Gram 1990

sheets of metal with a vacuum between them – have posed many manufacturing problems and require considerable development.

▌Transport

Transport is another huge user of energy and one that is facing enormous challenges over its contribution to global warming and other forms of pollution. For cars, the major battle is likely to be the improvement of fuel consumption: some engineers believe that a 100-mile-per-gallon car powered by a one-litre, turbo-charged diesel engine is not only practical but could solve many of the current environmental problems facing their industry. Such a car is likely to result as much from attention to aspects such as reducing weight with new materials and improving efficiency with better aerodynamics and minimized friction, as from adaptations to the engine itself.

Styling International's Concept 92 lightweight car, allowing for petrol, diesel, liquefied petroleum gas or battery power; drop-out engine permits use of state-of-the-art emissions monitoring equipment

With car engines, advances are being made through detail improvements such as the Design Council Award-winning Aeconoguide piston, whose complex shape reduces friction between the piston and the cylinder by up to 30 per cent, resulting in improved fuel consumption of around 3 per cent. The Aeconoguide was used in the Citroën AX which achieved as much as 112 miles per gallon in a run from John O'Groats to Land's End. Meanwhile Volkswagen is experimenting with a hybrid-fuel car designed specifically to meet the growing demand for quiet, pollution-free vehicles in the 'calm' areas that are now being created in many Continental towns and cities. This uses an electric motor for low-speed, in-town use and reverts to a petrol engine for conventional travel.

Electronic monitoring and microprocessor controls are also playing an increasing part in vehicle energy efficiency, and as this aspect becomes more

Stop/go energy recovery
Volvo has developed an energy recovery system for buses. The Cumulo hydraulic system is brought into operation electronically as soon as the driver applies the brakes, slowing the vehicle by absorbing energy to pump fluid from a reservoir to an accumulator where it pushes a piston to pressurize a gas. When the driver presses the accelerator, the pressurized gas reverses the direction of the piston and the fluid flows back to assist acceleration.

When using the Cumulo system, a half-full bus braking from 28 miles per hour can be brought back to 22 miles per hour from standstill before the engine is required to take over.

Source: *New Scientist*, 30 September 1989

important, there will also be an increased need for retrofitting existing products to improve performance. The kit produced by British design consultancy Ricardo-AS&A improves the aerodynamic performance of lorries. Costing around £1,900 to fit, it has been shown in wind tunnel and road tests to reduce fuel consumption by an average 19 per cent, with savings rising to 40 per cent for vehicles travelling at a steady 62 miles per hour.

Some, though not enough, progress is also being made in the air and at sea, again both by attention to design detail and by radical new thinking. For example, the company Airbus Industrie is experimenting with attaching an adhesive plastic film to most of the surfaces of its A320 aircraft. The film carries microscopic grooves which reduce drag by producing an orderly flow in the air next to the aircraft's skin, potentially reducing fuel consumption by as much as 1.5 per

Aerodynamic truck body system designed by Ricardo-AS&A

cent (giving annual fuel savings worth some £70,000 for a long-haul aircraft). At sea, it is the Japanese who have tackled the loss of energy due to cavitation and turbulence caused by ship's propellers. Both Mitsubishi and Ishikawajima-Harima have overcome the engineering problems of fitting twin contra-rotating propellers which improve fuel efficiency by around 15 per cent and offer advantages such as reduced vibration and noise.

There are, however, circumstances in which energy-saving is not the prime criterion in the choice of fuel. In 1988 a British Parliamentary Select Committee advocated electric propulsion for leisure boats operating on canals and other inland waterways, as the danger of water pollution from diesel or petrol boats is too high. As part of a research programme aimed at developing an electric canal boat that will run for a week without recharging its batteries, a new electric boat that can travel at almost 52 miles per hour has been built. This uses four motors with armatures shaped like a disc instead of a barrel to overcome the cooling problems that normally limit power output (*New Scientist*, 2 December 1989).

∎ Checklist

As energy use is the root cause of environmental threats such as global warming and pollution, designing products or equipment which are more energy efficient, or which can use alternative energy sources, should be the first priority for today's designers. Fortunately progress has already been made in some areas, but, for the majority of energy-dependent products, a great deal of research and development is still needed.

The following is a list of energy considerations that are relevant to many kinds of design:

1 Is a less environmentally-damaging fuel source available or can a fossil-fuel source be replaced with sustainable fuel?

2 If the chosen energy source is of fossil fuel origin, is there a risk that changes in taxation or pollution legislation will undermine the competitiveness of the product or service?

3 Could design adaptations reduce energy consumption?

4 Could alternative insulation, fittings or components reduce energy consumption?

5 Could improved monitoring and control systems reduce energy consumption?

6 Can any waste energy or excess heat output be recovered?

7 If not, can energy loss be minimized?

8 If the design might in the future be used with other products or components, is it compatible with those that are the most energy efficient?

4 Materials and packaging

In the green context, materials present the designer with some of the most difficult problems. The United Nations Environment Programme (UNEP) calculates that there are some 80,000 different chemicals in use in industry, with another thousand or so being added each year (Jacqueline Aloisi de Larderel, *Product Design and the Environment* UNEP presentation, Milan, February 1990). The choice of material (as with energy) is also made more complex by the fact that its origin is often as important as its qualities. Timber grown in a sustainable way is arguably the most environmentally desirable material of all, ameliorating global warming during its growth, but timber from non-sustainable sources (such as the tropical hardwoods used for furniture and interiors) amplifies the greenhouse effect, destroying wildlife habitats, and often causing catastrophic soil erosion, which blocks rivers and destroys potential for growing crops.

Any kind of presumption about materials can be dangerous. For example,

Seward Glynn Marsh's reception desk for Bank Negara Malaysia, made from sustainable woods backed by medium-density fibreboard

natural products are often believed to be environmentally preferable, but unbleached, undyed cotton, hailed as environmentally friendly by the fashion trade, depends on large quantities of hazardous chemicals (defoliants as well as pesticides and fertilisers) for its production and, in some parts of the world, requires high levels of irrigation that have resulted in substantial damage. (Watering the thirsty cotton crop in the Soviet Union is parching other crops and drying up the Aral Sea.)

■ Minimizing materials

For all designers, one of the first rules should be to minimize the quantity of any material chosen whenever possible. The benefits of this run right through the product's life, from the conservation of resources, through the reduction of energy and pollution in manufacture and use, to the minimization of the problems of disposal.

Minimizing materials demands careful attention to production processes as well as to the design itself. For example, when cut from sheet material, square shapes obviously utilize material more efficiently than circular shapes.

Lightweighting the product itself can achieve impressive results. A prime example is the British milk bottle. Careful design has reduced the weight of other

More calls for less paper

Telephone directories consume huge quantities of paper and other resources: British directories use 800 tonnes of ink every year. So when British Telecom commissioned Banks and Miles to redesign its directories, the twin objectives were effectiveness and economy.

More than a year's work produced amazing results: the new directories saved great quantities of paper, which brought massive reductions in transport and fuel costs, and have reduced the annual cost of printing phone directories by well over £1 million.

The major changes that have made these savings possible are the move from three to four columns of type and the dropping of repeat surnames, but the compaction this required to accommodate often long British addresses while retaining legibility required Banks and Miles to design a new typeface, itself only made possible by the move to computer typesetting.

The success of the new design was underlined by market research: over 80 per cent of users prefer the new directory.

Source: Banks & Miles 1990

drink containers too. A 1.5 litre PET (polyethyleneteraphthalate) bottle, which weighed 66 grams in 1980, weighed on average just 42 grams in 1989. More recently, CBM Engineering has introduced an aluminium can-making machine that reduces the amount of material needed by up to 6.5 per cent: the machine reforms the shape of the base to a profile that better withstands the internal pressure, thus enabling gauge thickness to be reduced.

The lighter pinta

Designers began looking for ways to reduce the weight of glass in the British milk bottle decades ago. Concentrating material where it was needed for strength and reducing it elsewhere cut the weight from 540 grams in the 1920s to around 520 grams in 1934. More improvements came in the 1960s, first with a narrow-mouthed design that weighed 370 grams and then, as the technology of coatings improved, with one of 340 grams.

The major change was the current 'pintie', introduced at the end of the 1960s. Based on the inherent strength of a circle, the design is in essence one circle sitting on top of another. The pintie weighed just 250 grams, reducing not just materials and energy but cutting the weight that had to be carried by roundsmen. Incremental improvements have recently reduced the weight to 230 grams.

Source: United Glass 1990

▌ Balancing the equation

Choosing the right material in any situation demands a careful balancing act. A look at the advantages and disadvantages of plastics in different situations provides an enlightening example of how the choice of one material or another should be governed by a thorough analysis of all the possible environmental implications.

Plastics have a substantial advantage when used for purposes where weight is critical to efficiency. This is obviously important in transport: the British Plastics Federation has estimated that the average 70 kilograms of plastics used in a car in place of heavier materials cuts fuel consumption by some 5 per cent (*Plastics Makes Progress Possible* factsheet, 1990); and the use of plastic bottles is saving thousands of pounds' worth of fuel for each airliner every year.

Plastics perform well on energy efficiency in general, despite their anti-environment image among many of the green pressure groups, some of whom seem to think that because most plastics come from oil they are to be avoided. In fact, plastics consume only about 4 per cent of all crude oil used, with 13 per cent going to petrol and by far the greatest quantity going to heat and power generation. What is more, the manufacture and processing of plastics is relatively energy efficient too: on average (and this will always depend on the methods used), using alternative packaging materials (the largest single use of plastics) would result in a doubling of energy consumption (*Packaging Saves Energy*, Industry Committee for Packaging and the Environment, 1985).

Why should materials such as these, which clearly have some definite environmental advantages, have such a poor environmental image? The reason is probably a combination of the widespread use of plastics for packaging and the durability of plastic litter. Plastic litter not only survives but floats in water, blows in the wind, and wraps itself around trees. This aspect of the plastics age has led the industry into a race to produce biodegradable plastics (see page 45), but in many cases there are better approaches than designing a product for one-trip biodegradability.

Plastics have been attacked for other reasons too. A particular target has been PVC (polyvinylchloride), partly because chlorine is used in its manufacture and partly because, when incinerated, it is seen as having the potential to produce hydrochloric acid and dioxins. This has led some countries, including Italy and Sweden, to consider banning the use of PVC. Yet, in practice, it is probably less harmful in overall environmental terms than some alternative materials. It is a low energy consumer and a low consumer of crude oil, because more than half of its composition consists of chlorine. This chlorine itself comes from salt

– a common material – and is a by-product of the manufacture of caustic soda, which in turn is essential for the manufacture of everything from paper to aluminium. What is more, when incinerated in a way which meets the relevant legal standards, dioxins are destroyed and the hydrochloric acid removed by the scrubbers that deal with acids from other materials too. By comparison other industries such as electroplating – which annually produces enough cyanide to kill everyone in Britain and North America – seem far more worthy of concern.

So the designer considering exploiting the hard-wearing, long-lasting properties of PVC should be less concerned than the designer of short-lived products – especially packaging – for which PVC is less likely to be the environmental answer since alternatives such as PET, being composed of only one polymer (unlike PVC and most other plastics), are easier to recycle.

The PVC story illustrates how different, and sometimes conflicting, considerations are involved in any decision about materials. The very qualities of long life and high strength-to-weight ratio that cause, for example, a litter problem may be those which make the material attractive in other areas, so designers and manufactuers should analyse every aspect and ensure that they have access to accurate and unbiased technical information.

▮ Using recycled materials

Designers and manufacturers should be increasingly aware of the possibility of using recycled materials. This is a different question from designing *for* recycling, as discussed in the next chapter. In general, materials that have come from a recycled source are more environmentally friendly than those from virgin sources. Not only does recycling reduce the waste that would otherwise have to be disposed of by incineration or dumping, but it is often far more energy efficient. For example, recycling paper can halve energy consumption compared with manufacture from trees; recycled glass uses as little as a quarter of the energy of first-time glass; and recycled aluminium can cut energy costs by up to 95 per cent.

Design specifications do not usually include the source of materials, as the performance of, for example, recycled steel, aluminium or glass is no different from that of virgin material, but some materials do require a special, and sometimes new, approach. For instance, recycled paper generally has somewhat different qualities to the virgin material and therefore also requires special treatment by the designer, which is unnecessary for the other three materials mentioned. Recycled plastics also create a need for designers to devise products that can be made successfully from low-grade material of limited colour choice. Such an approach is not easy. Finding viable uses for both low- and high-grade recycled materials is essential, and the more common this is, the more an appropriate infrastructure of recycling systems will make this approach economical.

Recycled paper is an example of a recycled material that raises complex issues and varies substantially in its greenness according to the processes involved. The recently introduced Conservation range of papers have been acclaimed for matching the quality of the best of virgin papers for such prestige purposes as annual reports. It achieves this by the careful selection of raw materials, using only high-quality white offcuts. It is obviously much easier to make a white or near-white paper from unprinted paper waste than from paper which has to be de-inked and bleached. Indeed, the double chlorine bleaching process sometimes used in paper recycling processes can produce up to twice the quantity of potentially damaging emissions as the process used for virgin paper manufacture. Some recycled paper manufacturers use hydrogen peroxide as an alternative, somewhat less damaging, bleaching agent, but designers should check details such as these with paper merchants when choosing paper.

In some areas, such as toilet and kitchen papers, recycled products can rapidly become commercially successful. Fort Sterling spent several years developing a paper recycling process that preserved the fibre length – and therefore the strength – of the original paper. Solving the problem in 1989 enabled them to launch Nouvelle, the first British toilet paper to be made entirely from recycled paper. Sainsbury's went one stage further and introduced a brand made from low-grade newspaper pulp, believing that their customers are now sufficiently environmentally educated to accept a paper marginally less attractive.

Examples of the many different grades of environment-friendly kitchen and toilet paper to be found on supermarket shelves

Recycled paper illustrates how, depending on processing methods and final use, recycled materials may sometimes be less environmentally friendly than they seem, but any recycled material should be investigated as a possible resource.

∎ Biodegradable materials

Biodegradable materials are another possible resource which demands careful consideration. Moves by the Italian government to outlaw non-degradable packaging (it had already imposed a 100 per cent tax on polythene bags) led the Italian manufacturer Ferruzzi to announce a new material for shopping bags in 1989. Previous degradables used relatively small quantities (around 10 per cent) of starch as a filler between webs of polyethylene: the starch degrades but not the poly-ethylene. The Ferruzzi material has a higher starch level and uses a short-chain polymer that breaks down more readily than polyethylene. Three months later the United States manufacturer Warner-Lambert went one better with a true biodegradable, Novon, which combines water and starch into thermoplastic pellets. ICI joined the race in 1990 with Biopol. Made by a bacterium from the fermentation of sugars, this (like Novon) is a true biodegradable, breaking down into carbon dioxide and water. It is already being used for hair shampoo bottles.

So should packaging designers specify biodegradables? Not accord-ing to the British government's Recycling Advisory Group, which warns that the by-products of some materials are not known, that starch-filled degradables can harm landfill sites, and that mixing degradables with other plastics waste inhibits recycling (*Greengauge*, 1 June 1990). Perhaps the biggest objection to degradables is that they

Shampoo bottles made from ICI's Biopol biodegradable plastic

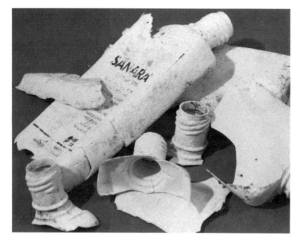

do little to alleviate the litter problem for which they are primarily designed: ICI claims that, 'Under favourable con-ditions such as those found in anaerobic sludge, Biopol can completely disappear in a matter of weeks' (ICI Biopol press release, April 1990), but this is a long time in the life of a shampoo bottle floating down a river. Materials such as these will undoubtedly prove extremely useful in some ways, but they risk encouraging a more careless attitude to litter and disposal than more durable, recyclable materials.

▎Finite resources

It is in the interests of designers and manufacturers to choose materials that are not suddenly going to run out. In the case of timber, with some 50 million acres of forest being destroyed every year, it is hardly surprising that some previously popular woods have already vanished and many more are threatened with commercial, or even actual, extinction. Indeed, the United Nations believes that almost none of the countries currently logging unsustainably will have any commercial timber left within ten years unless they change their practices fundamentally.

Although finite, the great majority of other mainstream raw materials, and the materials made from them, including ceramics, aluminium, glass and steel, are available in sufficient quantities for fears about their depletion to be minimal. However, designers should always investigate new materials, new uses and using smaller quantities to achieve more. The use of straw as raw material for paper, which provides an alternative use for a material too often burned (to the discomfort of local people), shows how new uses can often be environmentally beneficial. In the United States, an experiment is underway to make newsprint from Kenaf, a fast-growing annual plant that reaches 5–6 metres in a few months and can then be harvested for use as a pulp feedstock in place of trees that take some 25 years to reach maturity. Plastics do cause concern because of their dependence on cheap crude oil; however, it is possible that the increasing cost of oil will make recycling even more attractive and encourage the development of more plastics from sustainable biomass sources.

▍Finishes

The problems of choosing materials for a process or a finish can have immensely serious environmental implications. Take, for example, the field of paints and printing inks: both contain pigments, some of which are highly toxic and should ideally be avoided (for example, many yellow pigments rely on cadmium); both have traditionally also used solvents of various kinds, most of which have toxic potential and are causing increasing worldwide concern. Alternatives – usually water-based – are now becoming available in everything from paint systems for vehicle manufacturers and interiors to gravure printing inks. Even the mineral oil used as a base in other kinds of printing inks is being replaced with a greener alternative, such as Usher-Walker's range, which uses oil from the rape plant, though these often have a price premium initially.

▍Checklist

The rate of change in many materials fields is likely to accelerate in the near future as the demand for greener products and processes develops. Information about the environmental implications of materials must therefore extend rapidly too. (See Chapter 8)

The following checklist highlights the kinds of questions that designers and manufacturers should ask themselves when specifying and processing materials:

1 If the material comes from a scarce or seriously-declining source, is an alternative available?

2 Has proper consideration been given to pollution that may be caused either in the manufacture or disposal of the material?

3 Has the quantity of material used been minimized?

4 Are the materials the most energy-efficient in manufacture and final use?

5 Has the use of recycled materials been fully considered?

6 Is there a significant risk of environmental protection laws in any proposed market either seriously constraining the use of the chosen materials or increasing their production or disposal costs?

7 Has your company established a system for checking and collating information about the environmental implications of different materials?

5 The product lifecycle

Environmental concerns have extended rather than altered fundamentally decisions about materials, efficiency and cost. Lifecycle decisions are different. Traditionally, the concern of the designer has ended with the launch of the product, but the green designer should think about its complete life from cradle to grave.

BMW chairman Eberhard von Kuenheim summed up this change when speaking in the United States early in 1990:

> Vehicle makers have a responsibility to their product at the end of the life cycle . . . Automotive engineers should be concerned not only with the construction but with the destruction of the automobile. (*Financial Times*, 6 January 1990)

BMW became the first car manufacturer to build its own facility (at Wackersdorf in Germany) for disassembling old vehicles and reclaiming parts and materials for recycling. The company has also collaborated with General Electric in a search

From each used catalytic converter Mercedes-Benz extract 5gms of platinum and 1gm of rhodium

for plastic car materials that can be more easily recycled.

∎ The end of landfill tipping

The automotive industry's nightmare vision of vast piles of unrecyclable scrap vehicles disfiguring the landscape is beginning to haunt other industries too, partly because the public have a natural abhorrence of the whole notion of waste, but also because the customary answer of burying waste and forgetting it is becoming more expensive and problematic. Landfill sites are becoming difficult to find in many countries, and their operations are being made more expensive as governments take action to try to avoid long-term pollution risks. A draft European Community Directive on landfill sites published in mid-1990 could vastly increase the costs of running Britain's thousands of waste dumps and lead to a total ban on the dumping of liquid wastes.

The problem is immense: 120 million tonnes of waste is produced in the UK every year, less than 2 per cent of which is recycled. The potential for improvement is huge too: every household throws away the equivalent of six trees, 32 kilograms of metal, 47 of plastics and 74 of glass annually. The British government has set a target of recycling a half of all recyclable waste by the turn of the century and is discussing the imposition of levies on raw materials to encourage recycling. Elsewhere in Europe, governments are imposing levies of up to £80 per tonne on dumped waste. People in the United States throw away three times as much domestic rubbish and five times as much commercial rubbish as the British. In 1989, less than 10 per cent of the US mountain of rubbish was recycled, but recent amendments to the Resources Conservation and Recovery Act stipulate a 25 per cent target for recycling by 1992

(*Financial Times* 31 October 1989, Department of the Environment October 1989).

Designers have a key role in minimizing the harm caused to the environment by a product which is no longer useful. Incentives for recycling and against dumping are likely to increase significantly during the 1990s, but it is wrong to see recycling or easy disposal as the only, or even the most important, concerns for the green designer. The first consideration should be the life of the product itself.

∎ Product life

For products that are designed as use-once-and-throw-away items, the designer and manufacturer must ask if this is the best answer. For example, can one-trip packaging be replaced with refillable containers? The Body Shop has shown that at least some consumers are very happy to replace aerosols with pump-action, refillable sprays, while a German company is experimenting with a re-usable PET bottle. As environmental concern increases, it seems likely that use-once products that have no health or similar justification will become increasingly unpopular.

Occasionally such products can have a secondary use – container jars that became drinking glasses were once quite common – but such an approach (except perhaps in the Third World, where people are often forced to adapt anything that comes to hand to boost their meagre resources) tends to be artificial and unlikely to make any real contribution to the longevity of a product, either because performance in the secondary use is diminished or because it is simply too unattractive. In practice, a balance has to be struck between the design life of the product, including such considerations as likely future improvements in technical or safety standards, and the degree of extra energy or materials needed to extend a product's life. What is essential – and this is nothing new – is to ensure that weak points in a design are eliminated so that, as far as possible, it does not fail before the end of its design life.

▋ Maintenance and repair

Design for ease of maintenance and repair is also important for a green product. A recent survey (*New Scientist*, 24 December 1988) of domestic appliances found on rubbish dumps showed that an extraordinarily high percentage had very little wrong with them and could have been easily and cheaply repaired; indeed, a significant number merely required a new fuse.

For many products – washing machines and dishwashers, sound reproduction systems, video recorders – the kinds of microprocessor self-diagnosis systems being provided increasingly in vehicles and personal computers are likely to make the diagnosis of faults relatively simple. Where practical, the designer should exploit this by designing both the product and the instruction manual to help an unskilled person carry out the repair, for it is often the difficulty and cost of obtaining a satisfactory repair service that encourages the premature discarding of such products. Where professional repair is required, the ability to identify the faulty part – even the model number of the machine – can save time and cost and should therefore be considered at the design stage. Certain construction methods are anathema not just to those wishing to repair products but also to those involved at the end of the product's life in disassembly for remanufacture and recycling. Rivets are a pet hate both of recyclers and repairers, while the bundling of a component that may need replacing with others that have little likelihood of failure is just as unhelpful.

∎ Design for upgrading

Many products are a combination of high and low technology. This can
create a new approach to design for
extended product life. There are likely to
be sound technical reasons why the high
technology element of the design should
be regularly updated, but the more basic
elements may well be capable of longer
life. If the shorter-life elements are
designed on a modular basis, it may be
possible to update a product without
throwing the whole thing away. For
example, while computers are regularly
enhanced with the addition of plug-in
boards, there is usually little real reason
why this cannot be extended so that new

Something new, something old
Working with the Product Lifecycle Institute
in Geneva, Agfa-Gevaert has developed a
modular design for its photocopiers that
enables key elements to be upgraded while
the parts that usually wear out – such as the
drum – have been redesigned to ensure long
life. This has considerably increased the life
of the basic product without inhibiting
improved performance: compared with an
average three- to five-year life for most
photocopiers, the Agfa-Gevaert machines
have an average life of six to ten years.

The machines are leased and can be
returned or exchanged at any time: each has
an average of 2.5 clients during its lifetime,
making long-term quality of performance
crucial to the manufacturer if lifetime costs
are not to become a drain on profits.

Source: Institut für Produktdauerforschung,
Geneva, June 1990

generations of computer technology are housed in old-generation
boxes and even use some of the other hardware, such as the drives, the
performance of which tends to be upgraded less frequently. The same
thinking is applicable to appliances such as washing machines, where
more sophisticated (and energy-efficient) control systems may become
available but the casing (and even the mechanical items, if designed for
a long enough life) can continue to serve their purpose.

With the exception of aircraft and shipping – where

re-engining or the introduction of other kinds of new and advanced equipment is commonplace – such an approach is so far rare. One company that has investigated the possibilities is Agfa-Gevaert, spurred on by the fact that it leases its photocopiers and therefore has an interest in reducing lifetime costs rather than being concerned only with the purchase price. This is a policy which could in the future be extended to many other types of products.

∎ Component recovery

Products which have reached the end of their useful lives will in most cases contain components or assemblies that are far from worn out or outdated. If the product has been properly designed with a concern to minimize environmental damage, then these units should be easily removable either for use as straight replacements for new parts or for remanufacture and re-use.

Remanufacture itself is becoming a more important element in extending the life of components. The modern remanufacturing industry is very different from the old suppliers of reconditioned parts, using sophisticated machining and test equipment to remake products that really are as good as new. In some industries – especially car manufacturing – it is likely that designers will have to take into account the needs of the remanufacturers from the start of considering a new product. In other areas of design, the most likely impact of component recovery and remanufacture is that they provide a new source of components for new products that have the potential of being relatively inexpensive, but systems to ensure quality and continuity of supply need to be established before mass production items can depend on such an approach.

Nevertheless, as purchasers become more aware of lifetime costs and as components become more valuable, remanufacture and re-use seem likely to increase. Michael Henstock, one of Britain's leading experts on design for recycling and author of *Design for Recyclability*, has suggested that major components might be bar-coded to help recyclers identify and sort scrap materials.

■ Designing for materials recycling

One of the first aims in designing in a way which will facilitate future recycling is to do everything possible to prevent quality materials being degraded unnecessarily. Copper is extremely difficult to remove in the steel recycling process, and a mere 0.2 per cent of copper can cause severe cracking in the finished steel: so, while scrap steel is worth around £100 a tonne and copper about £1,000 a tonne when separate, the two together are worth only about £50 a tonne (British Steel 1990).

A similar problem arises with other materials. PET, for example, is potentially excellent for recycling but, again, certain contaminants can spoil the scrap for the recycler. The main problem, however, is other

Steel can separator

kinds of plastic, which tend to have roughly the same density of PET and which – unlike, for example, aluminium caps – are difficult to separate. Some PET bottles – but not all – have a tiny non-PET plastics sealing ring beneath the cap which causes a similar problem for the recycler as copper in steel scrap. Recycling machines which can identify different chemical markers in plastics are gradually being developed, but many problems still need to be solved.

The first rule for a designer wishing to assist the recycler is therefore to reduce and rationalize the choice of materials. This requires an understanding of the interaction of materials in the recycling process. Fortunately, such advice is generally easier to obtain than information about the other environmental implications of materials: both the materials industries and the recyclers are helpful.

In many cases, the use of alternative materials can facilitate recycling. For example, aluminium is readily removed from steel scrap in the remelting process and can sometimes therefore provide an alternative to copper. Another approach is to design the product so that the incompatible materials can easily be separated at the recycling stage. Again using copper as the example, if all the copper wiring can be removed as a single loom from a washing machine or car (and providing that other major part-copper components such as electric motors can be separated simply too), the problem may be overcome. Such an approach is also useful for the reclamation of materials that may be small in quantity but are either rare – and therefore valuable – or potentially hazardous.

As in many other areas of design, designing for recycling does demand compromise. For instance, the green designer who succeeds in reducing the thickness of metal used in a beverage can will find the recyclers complaining that this leads to the protective coating forming a higher percentage of the scrap material, thus complicating the recycling process. Again, the plastics recycling industry would ideally like products to be made not only of one kind of plastic but in a single colour too.

∎ Consumer sorting

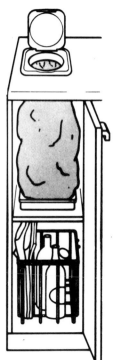

Designers also have a role in improving the products and systems that are now becoming available to help the public collect their waste in a way that best assists recycling. The need to identify, separate and store different kinds of waste is presenting entirely new problems for designers of rubbish bins, kitchens and supermarkets alike. Particularly on the Continent and in North America, there are already instances where large quantities of a single material is collected relatively easily and profitably from homes, offices and factories. In Britain, Dow Chemicals has launched a scheme to collect some of the three billion plastic cups thrown away in offices and factories each year, while Lin Pac Plastics International has started a similar scheme to collect the polystyrene foam food packaging trays used in McDonald's fast food restaurants (*Greengauge*, 18 May 1990).

Better Bin for domestic rubbish sorting

Despite these initiatives, overall progress is slow and improved schemes supported by the appropriate collection equipment and facilities are needed to encourage the routine recycling of waste material.

∎ Checklist

All the efforts of designers, manufacturers and recyclers will never prevent some materials being left for ultimate disposal. Since the biggest environmental threat is pollution, whether through dumping or incineration, this should influence decisions about materials and ideally designs should provide also for elements contaminated in use by pollutants being eventually removed for separate treatment.

The following is a list of the main points which should be considered when the different environmental implications of a product's whole lifecycle are being thought through:

1   Has the ideal.life for the product been assessed from an environmental point of view?

2   Has the design been reviewed and tested to eliminate weaknesses?

3   Can the product be easily maintained and repaired?

4   Where appropriate, does the instruction manual encourage repair rather than replacement?

5   Can the life of the product be extended by allowing the replacement of components or systems that are likely to become outdated?

6   Once its prime use is ended, can the product have a useful second purpose?

7   Has the product been designed to simplify disassembly for recycling or for the recovery of components and sub-assemblies for re-use or remanufacture?

8   Does the combination of materials create difficulties for recycling? If so, can alternatives be used instead?

9   Have any hazards that may cause difficulties at the end of the product's life been designed out or isolated for easy separation?

10 Has the design been checked in the context of a regular review of the manufacturer's overall waste stream?

6 The green message

How is the consumer to know whether or not a product is environmentally acceptable? The first response of many advertising and marketing people to the sudden popularity of environmental issues was to introduce the words 'environment-friendly' at every opportunity. The second response was to invent a labelling scheme. Both have been the subject of abuse but have fortunately prompted attempts to legitimize claims and provide some genuine assistance for the consumer looking for information about the effects of products on the environment.

The most effective safeguards against ludicrous claims – in Britain, at least – have so far come from the risk of ridicule: the Friends of the Earth Green Con awards have justly received considerable media attention, while the Consumers Association has been equally scathing about some claims. As a result, most companies are now being more circumspect. ICI, for example, removed the 'environmentally friendly' tag from a cleaning liquid not because the liquid was damaging but because the factory producing it had polluted a local river.

■ Label schemes

Most consumers still have to rely on the integrity of the manufacturers and retailers for positive help. The Safeway supermarket group is just

Safeway recycled paper logo

one of the retailers to have introduced its own labelling scheme, with a logo to indicate that a product has some environment-friendly attribute and a slogan such as 'recycled paper' describing it. 'It is part of our policy to show customers what the goods are and how they are environmentally friendly,' explained a Safeway spokesperson, confirming that environmentally questionable products such as batteries and disposable nappies would be eligible for the labels if, respectively, they were free of heavy metals or dioxins (*Design Week*, 12 January 1990).

Soap and detergent manufacturer Procter & Gamble has responded to the burgeoning competition from self-styled green alternatives by providing two kinds of environmental information on its washing and cleaning products. The first lists attributes such as biodegradability and the use of recycled materials in the packaging, and the second catalogues the ingredients and describes their function. Nevertheless, consumers are still left to interpret for themselves claims that Ariel uses 'less resources than conventional powders'.

Widely used recycling logo

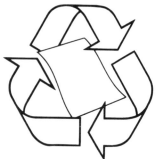

There is also a considerable risk from labels such as the rapidly-spreading recycling logo, the use of which is uncontrolled and can therefore be meaningless, although some helpful, unofficial schemes, aiming to provide the facts and publish the criteria by which they are used, do exist. A group of UK recycled paper suppliers has also taken a welcome step towards overcoming the confusion about what the word 'recycled' means when applied to paper. Their classification system describes not only the type of pulp and its constituents, but also guarantees that at least

75 per cent of the raw material is from recycled sources.

More formal action to eliminate abuses is also being taken, especially in the field of television advertising. The British Independent Television Association has published guidelines covering the environmental claims made by television advertisers. These require factual evidence for claims and include the tough warning that:

> Categorical statements such as 'environment friendly', 'safe' or 'green' are unlikely to be appropriate to any mass-produced product. (*Copy Clearance Bulletin*, Independent Television Association, June 1990)

Tesco biodegradable logo

The European Commission has a slightly different approach: its television Directive includes the injunction that television advertising 'shall not encourage behaviour prejudicial to health and safety or to the protection of the environment' (*Official Journal of the European Communities*, 17 October 1989).

In some countries labelling schemes backed by law have been introduced. The first and best known is the German Blue Angel scheme, but there are others in countries as far apart as Australia, Canada and Japan.

German Blue Angel environment-friendly logo

Significantly, some of these schemes place as much emphasis on improving the awareness of the public about the relationship between the environment and the products they buy as on the labelling scheme itself.

It is too early to see exactly what form future labelling schemes are likely to take, but clearly standardization is vital, and no satisfactory scheme will be simple. The British government has at least backed away from its original suggestion that a new Europe-wide scheme should assess products only on the environmental implications of their use or disposal. The West German Blue Angel scheme, on the other hand, has, since the end of the 1970s, moved from an assessment of a single green aspect (such as recycling or energy efficiency) to an assessment of the impact of a product from cradle to grave – but even this ignores other aspects such as the environmental performance of manufacture and distribution.

In the long term, an environmental assessment scheme on similar lines to the British Standard for Quality Systems seems to offer the best hope for a solution. With the growing impact of company-wide environmental audits, such an approach is becoming feasible and would have the benefit of measuring not just the company's overall performance but also its ability to manage the achievement of high standards of environmental responsibility on a continuing basis. This kind of assessment would undoubtedly have to include the company's design and product development policies. Companies which achieved acceptable environmental standards would then officially be allowed to publicize the fact on their products.

What is not in doubt is the impact on designers and manufacturers of the labelling schemes and controls on advertising. Designers have become used to having to include all kinds of health information on food and other packaging, usually in forms laid down by legislation. Such constraints are likely to increase in the future to take account of environmental impact information. There are also likely to be increased restrictions on the way in which products can be promoted. Banning the use of phrases such as 'environmentally friendly' on high-performance cars, as recommended in the EC Directive, is just a start: it is likely that some visual devices implying greenness will be banned too. Indeed, if the EC Directive is to be taken literally, advertisements encouraging a car to be driven in a way that is not fuel-efficient are also likely to be proscribed.

∎ Efficient communication

Designers should not see their role solely as one of responding to green rules and pressures, for they have a positive role to play in promoting environmentally sympathetic behaviour too. For example, energy conservation in the home generally requires people to use their heating systems and domestic appliances in a way that minimizes energy consumption: heating programmers that are easier to understand and use would encourage efficiency; and the energy implications of choosing different programmes or different temperature settings on other equipment could be made much more obvious to the householder in order to encourage both financial and energy savings. Ensuring that safety instructions or sign systems are easy to read and attractive to the eye is also a crucial way of protecting both the environment and users of products and machinery.

Whether it be the design of products and systems that encourages people to collect waste for recycling or the promotion of greener behaviour through the careful design of instructions and manuals, the creativity of designers is much needed in persuading and helping people to minimize the damage that they cause to the environment whilst still improving the quality of life in general.

7 Green ethics

Environmental issues raise both ethical and business questions but these do not necessarily conflict. As Niels Peter Flint of the pioneering European green design group O_2 put it, 'If we continue to destroy the world, there won't be one to make money in' (*Design Week*, 6 October 1989).

▌ Codes of conduct

Perhaps surprisingly, the seven leading economic nations (the so-called G7 group) appear to agree, enough to inspire a Code of Environmental Practice, submitted to the G7 heads of state, that has at its heart a commitment to the stewardship of living and non-living systems of the earth in order to maintain their sustainability for the present and the future, allowing development with equity. The Code calls for:

> . . . full accounting costs to ensure that the stock of renewable resources is maintained, with waste and pollution kept below the assimilative capacity of the environment and non-renewable resources either substituted or harvested at the lowest rate possible.

The Code goes on to reject 'anthropocentric utilitarianism and undiluted ecocentrism as, by themselves, both inadequate and dangerous' (*habitat*, Environment Council, June 1990).

Many professional design bodies have long taken the view that designers have a responsibility not just to their clients and their staff but to society as a whole – fortunately using rather more straightforward words than the G7 governments. As long ago as 1987, the International Federation of Interior Designers and Architects adopted a code of conduct calling on designers to 'accept professional responsibility to act in the best interest of ecology and the environment'.

In Britain, the Environmental and Energy Policy Committee of the Royal Institute of British Architects (RIBA) has recommended that RIBA's practice documents should make all members responsible for persuading their clients to permit the use of environmentally benign materials and the employment of energy-efficient specification and construction. Further detailed amendments would guide architects on everything from the specification of energy controls to the avoidance of specified materials that use CFCs. The British Chartered Society of Designers has taken a more general approach in its 1990 draft Code of Conduct:

> Members shall have due regard to the effect of their work and endeavour that it may cause as little harm as possible either directly or indirectly to the ecology or environment, including living creatures; endangered species of plant or fauna; the atmosphere, rivers and seas. Members shall wherever possible encourage the conservation of energy and the recycling of used products, packaging and materials.

It is the spirit of such codes that matters, for the actual wording will always be open to discussion and can never cover every eventuality. Although providing useful signals, they can never remove the need for individual designers to take their own ethical decisions.

The Director of the Industry and Environment Office of the United Nations Environment Programme, Jacqueline Aloisi de Larderel, recognizes the problems:

> There is as yet no comprehensive analytical method currently in use to determine which product is more holistically environmentally sound than another, although such integrated environmental analysis is beginning.

She goes on to explain that, even if such methods can be developed for more complex products, individuals will still have to make difficult value judgements such as weighing damage to rainforests against the effects of toxic emissions (*Product Design and the Environment*, Milan, February 1990).

▮ Which shade of green?

Faced with a client or employer whose activities are distinctly unfriendly to the environment, what should one do? The easy answer is to repeat all the commercial arguments for going green and to point out the potential long-term benefits of adopting a comprehensive green product development policy – but what if the client or the board of directors is just not interested or is in a business that thrives on the creation of unnecessary waste? Some designers may decide that they will take a moral stand and avoid such clients or product areas, preferring to concentrate on projects which could be particularly beneficial to, for example, the Third World. Others may feel that they are in no position to choose, but whatever one's responsibilities or commitments, progress can be made in almost every area by putting into action or applying more rigorously the principles outlined in this book.

▮ Your own back yard

There are two other important areas of concern for the ethical green designer. Firstly, all designers should take a look at all their own activities and establish how they can limit environmental damage from day to day. Every kind of company should undertake environmental audits, which should cover everything from the energy efficiency of the office heating and lighting systems to the use of recycled drawing or computer paper and the environmental standards of the company bike or car. Such audits should also analyse professional philosophy, resources and level of access to, up-to-date information sources. Environmentally responsible design requires a clear policy, a structured approach and reliable, unbiased information.

Precious metals extracted from catalytic converter coatings

The second need is training. In Britain and elsewhere, few designers – whether they are working in engineering, industrial design, graphics

or any other field – receive any real introduction to either the theory or practice of environmentally sympathetic design. In Britain, there has been an upswell of interest in green design among students, especially those on arts-based courses, but most teachers are floundering, for the subject is as new to them as to those wishing to study it. Only cooperation between industry, the design professions, and the teachers and colleges can produce the combination of objectives, structures and resources to fill this vital gap.

8 Information sources

Although there is still a great lack of detailed information and advice on many environmental issues, some useful help is available. The lack of appropriate information for designers about materials has now been recognized and some major initiatives are being taken to fill at least some of the other gaps. The chemical and related industries are relatively well served and have considerable information available, although research is not merely providing knowledge about new products but rather causing a re-assessment of existing advice. Compared with many other areas of design, architects are also relatively well served, with some useful information already obtainable, particularly on different types of timber.

The following is a selective list of some of the publications and organizations likely to be helpful.

▮ Publications

Books

Counsell, S (1990) *The Good Wood Guide*, London, Friends of the Earth – provides basic information about the alternatives to tropical hardwoods and lists suppliers and other companies who have qualified for the FoE Good Wood Seal of Approval.

Department of Environment (1990), *This Common Heritage*, London, HMSO – British Government White Paper and its first comprehensive policy statement, including detailed proposals for tackling such problems as industrial pollution. Also indicates possible future action in other areas such as transport.

Environmental Bureau (1989) *Green Index*, London, Cassell – directory of environmental organizations in Britain and Ireland, covering mainly ecological/wildlife groups but also some industrial organizations.

Fox, A and Murrell, R (1989) *Green Design*, London, Architecture Design and Technology Press – a guide to the environmental impact of building materials. Provides a useful starting-point for architects and product designers.

Henstock, M (1988) *Design for Recyclability*, London, Institute of Metals – an excellent guide to the ways in which designers can assist recycling, especially in the automotive and domestic appliance industries.

Institution of Mechanical Engineers (1990) *Greenhouse Effect Sourcebook*, London, Institution of Mechanical Engineers Information and Library Service – lists useful information about key environmental problems and includes more than 250 abstracts.

Pearce, D, Markandya, A and Barbier, E (1989) *Blueprint for a Green Economy*, London, Earthscan Publications – originally commissioned by the British Department of the Environment, this report sets the scene for major changes in the impact of taxation and fiscal policies on industrial activities that affect the environment.

Rosehaugh plc (1990) *Buildings and Health: the Rosehaugh Guide for Clients, Specifiers and Construction Professionals*, London, RIBA Publications – assesses the environmental implications of building materials.

Turner, K (ed) (1988) *Sustainable Environmental Management*, London, Bellhaven Press – the result of research into environmental economics sponsored by the Economic and Social Research Council, this book provides a well-argued and detailed analysis of the principles of sustainability, in terms of economic growth through the utilization of resources, and of development based on concepts of ethical duty to future generations.

Van Weenen, J C (1990) *Waste Prevention: Theory and Practice*, The Hague, Netherlands, CIP-Gegevens Koninklijke Bibliotheek – probably the most comprehensive book on this subject, ranging from the role of design in such industries as furniture and electronics to the current and prospective policies of governments throughout the world. Available in English.

Periodicals

Energy Management, Department of Energy, Room 341, 1 Palace Street, London SW1E 5HE – free, monthly magazine containing case studies on ways in which industry and commerce are saving money through energy conservation.

Environmental Law Bulletin, McKenna & Co, Inveresk House, 1 Aldwych, London WC2R 0HF – published every two months by solicitors specializing in environmental cases. Includes brief summaries of recent environmental developments. Available free but selectively.

Greengauge, 12 Bolton Street, London W1Y 7PA – fortnightly newsletter that provides a full, but uncritical, digest of environmental news, concentrating on information with an industrial or commercial relevance.

New Scientist, 35 Perrymount Road, Haywards Heath, West Sussex RH16 3DH – weekly magazine giving valuable international overview combining information about technological and scientific developments with news from the environmental and political fronts.

▌Organizations

British Powder Metal Federation, Ashton Court, 67a Compton Road, Wolverhampton WV3 9QZ (tel 0902 28987) – produces information resources including a video explaining how the use of powder metal technology can significantly reduce input materials in the manufacture of complex shapes. The Federation also has available a *Designing for Powder Technology* manual and a free booklet on the process.

British Plastics Federation, 5 Belgrave Square, London SW1X 8PD (tel 071-235 9483) – can provide a list of companies recycling plastics.

Building Research Establishment (BRE), Garston, Watford WD2 7JR (tel 0923 664258) – Building Energy Efficiency Division offers a wealth of publications, some free, on all aspects of energy conservation relevant to buildings, including a method of assessing the environmental quality of a building at the design stage. The BRE also offers advisory services of various kinds.

Can Makers Information Service, 36 Grosvenor Gardens, London SW1W 0EB (tel 071-629 9621) – provides useful information and advice about recycling and other environmental aspects of cans.

Centre for Alternative Technology, Machynlleth, Powys SY20 9AZ (tel 0654 2400) – offers services on alternative technologies, especially renewable energy sources, domestic energy conservation, energy-efficient buildings and sewage treatment. Services range from full consultancy to residential courses and publications.

Copper Development Association, Orchard House, Mutton Lane, Potters Bar, Hertfordshire EN6 3AP (tel 0707 50711) – provides technical advice and information on aspects of copper use. Free information sheets include a series on solar heating.

The Design Council, 28 Haymarket, London SW1Y 4SU (tel 071-839 8000) – offers two services of particular relevance to green design. The Designer Selection Service can recommend design consultants with expertise ranging from pollution control to packaging. The Materials Information Service provides information and advice on engineering materials use and processing, as well as operating a signposting service for industrial enquirers seeking detailed help. It can also provide general information on recyclability, physical properties, processing and finishing. The Design Council has offices throughout the United Kingdom.

The Environment Council, 80 York Way, London N1 9AG (tel 071-278 4736) – runs a Business and Environment Programme that offers helpful information, conferences and briefings. The Programme includes specific references to design.

Friends of the Earth (FoE), 26-28 Underwood Street, London N1 7JQ (tel 071-490 1555) – probably Britain's most useful environmental pressure group as far as design is concerned: FoE bases its campaigns on careful research and often supports them with information that is constructive (see *Good Wood Guide*, page 73). Its extensive publications list ranges from inexpensive popular guides to books aimed at professionals.

Green Alliance, 49 Wellington Street, London WC2E 7BN (tel 071-836 0341) – runs an Industry and Environment programme that aims to encourage a dialogue between industrialists and environmentalists. Policy advice available for the industry.

GreenNet, 25 Downham Road, London N1 5AA (tel 071-249 2948) – an international computer network intended for anyone with an interest in environmental and related issues. The UN Conference of Environment and Development ('ECO 92), to be held in 1992, will be prepared and publicized via EcoNet, part of the GreenNet system. The International Council of Societies of Industrial Design (ICSID) will also be using the network for sharing information and publicizing events.

Industry Committee for Packaging and the Environment (Incpen), 10 Greycoat Place, London SW1P 1SB (tel 071-222 8866) – set up by the packaging industry in 1974 in response to attacks from FoE, the organization now produces useful information about the resources used by packaging and the benefits that packaging can bring in, for example, preventing food wastage.

International Tin Research Institute, Kingston Lane, Uxbridge, Middlesex UB8 3PJ (tel 0895 72406) – provides information on environmental and other aspects of materials and processes using tin, including recycling, non-toxic coatings and brazing alloys.

Laboratory of the Government Chemist, Queens Road, Teddington, Middlesex TW11 0LY (tel 081-943 7000) – offers a range of services to industry, including the provision of impartial analysis and advice relevant to environmentally satisfactory products and buildings.

Metal Finishing Association, 27 Frederick Street, Birmingham B1 3HJ (tel 081-236 2657) – provides technical advice on various kinds of coating, together with information about suppliers.

National Physical Laboratory (NPL), Teddington, Middlesex TW11 0LW (tel 081-977 3222) – responsible for developing and maintaining the UK's primary measurement standards for physical and engineering quantities, including the provision of standard gas mixtures for the calibration of pollution monitoring equipment. NPL also provides standards and measurement techniques covering other environmental issues including noise, radioactivity and electromagnetic interference.

Network for Environmental Technology Transfer (NETT), 207 Avenue Louise, bte 10, B-1050, Brussels, Belgium (tel 32 2 645 0940) – set up with the help of the European Community. Offers three databanks of information about companies and organizations in the environmental field; about relevant European Community law and programmes; and about primarily technical aspects of the environment in general.

Plastics and Rubber Advisory Service, 5 Belgrave Square, London SW1X

8PD (tel 071-235 9483) – offers free advice on materials, manufacturing methods and suppliers, and on plastics recycling.

Plastics and Rubber Institute, 11 Hobart Place, London SW1W 0HL (tel 071-245 9555) – the professional institute for those working in the polymer industry and educational establishments. Organizes conferences and meetings on subjects including recycling and biodegradability.

Stainless Steel Advisory Centre, PO Box 161, Shepcote Lane, Sheffield S9 1TR (tel 0742 440060) – provides free advice on the selection, design and surface finish of stainless steel.

UK Centre for Economic and Environmental Development (CEED), 19 Upper Belgrave Street, London SW1X 8BA (tel 071-245 6441) – set up to develop policies which further the economic well-being of the UK and protect its environment for the future through the sustainable use of resources. Activities include the publication of a *bulletin* and the organization of conferences on industry and environment-related issues.

United Kingdom Reclamation Council, 16 High Street, Brampton, Huntingdon PE18 8TU (tel 0480 55249) – provides information about what can be recycled and about sources of recycled materials.

Watt Committee on Energy, Savoy Hill House, Savoy Hill, London WC2R 0BU (tel 071-379 6875) – promotes and assists research and development and the dissemination of knowledge concerning energy. Its well-researched reports cover a wide field, from renewable energy sources and the influence of electronics on energy costs, to small-scale hydro power and responses to the greenhouse effect. Membership consists of some 60 professional institutions.

■ Financial assistance

Enterprise Initiative (tel 0800 585794) – run by the Department of Trade and Industry (DTI). Offers subsidized consultancy to small- and medium-sized companies, including help on environmental problems relating to product design and manufacture, and waste minimization. The DTI also runs a number of other assistance schemes that have applications to design and the environment.

Environmental Protection Technology Scheme (tel 071-276 8318) – run by the Department of Environment. Offers 50 per cent grants for the development of technologies to deal with pollution. The first project to be funded provided almost 200,000 for the DCE Group Ltd to develop a new type of filter for reducing dust emissions from municipal incinerators.

Euroenviron (tel DTI Environmental Enquiry Point 0800 585794) – programme offering up to 50 per cent government funding for collaborative research and development aimed at boosting environmental technologies. Collaboration must be with a partner from another European Community or EFTA country. Part of the Eureka programme.